RAYMOND BRIGGS
Unlucky Wally

HAMISH HAMILTON
London

Other Books by Raymond Briggs

THE STRANGE HOUSE
MIDNIGHT ADVENTURE
SLEDGES TO THE RESCUE
*
RING-A-RING O'ROSES
THE WHITE LAND
FEE FI FO FUM
*
THE MOTHER GOOSE TREASURY
THE FAIRY TALE TREASURY
*
THE ELEPHANT AND THE BAD BABY *text by Elfrida Vipont*
THE TALE OF THREE LANDLUBBERS *text by Ian Serraillier*
JIM AND THE BEANSTALK
*
FATHER CHRISTMAS
FATHER CHRISTMAS GOES ON HOLIDAY
FUNGUS THE BOGEYMAN
THE SNOWMAN
THE SNOWMAN POP-UP
GENTLEMAN JIM
THE FUNGUS THE BOGEYMAN PLOP-UP BOOK
*
WHEN THE WIND BLOWS
THE TIN POT FOREIGN GENERAL AND THE OLD IRON WOMAN

First published in Great Britain 1987 by
Hamish Hamilton Ltd
27, Wrights Lane, London, W8 5TZ
Copyright © 1987 by Raymond Briggs
All rights reserved

British Library Cataloguing in Publication Data
Briggs, Raymond
Unlucky Wally
823′.914[F]   PR6052.R444
ISBN 0-241-12106-X

Printed in Italy by
Mondadori Editore, Verona

Wally Burke is always called Unlucky Wally.

He is unlucky with his ears.

He is unlucky with his teeth.

He is unlucky with his legs.

His nose is none too good either.

3

If Wally goes on holiday his room will be over-run with Spiders.

At night, Big Bats will get in and flap about his head.

In the morning, he will discover that the bed is full of Fleas.

At breakfast, the man opposite him will be eating with Long Black Finger Nails.

If Wally swims in the sea, he is bound to get covered in Tar.

When he comes out he is bound to tread on a Jelly Fish.

If Wally paddles in a pond, the Leeches will find him.

If Wally swims in a lake, he usually finds the Frog Spawn.

Afterwards, there is always Tapioca for tea.

In a restaurant, he is always put next to a man eating Snails;

or next to two men eating Jellied Eels.

Wally can never escape the smell of Boiled Cabbage.

If Wally has soup, the soup is bound to have a long Greasy Hair in it.

13

If Wally has a lettuce sandwich, it is bound to have Slugs in it.

If Wally bites into a meat pie, Maggots will come wriggling out of it. And if Wally fries an egg, before he can find the salt and pepper, the egg will be covered in Cockroaches.

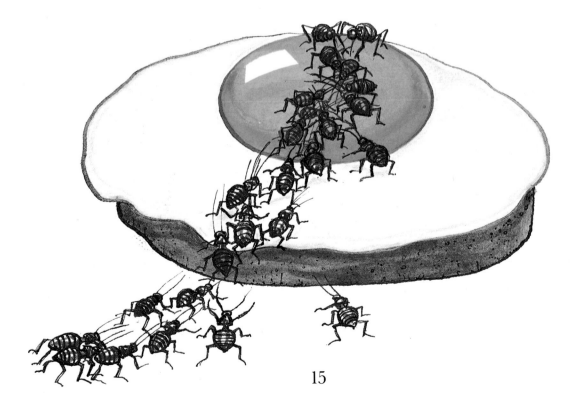

15

If Wally goes into a public lavatory, the inevitable leaking pipe will drip only on *his* head.

When Wally goes to bed in winter, hibernating Earwigs swarm into his ears,

and when Wally goes camping in summer, snakes get up his pyjama legs.

17

In towns, the pigeons find Wally.

In the country, Wally finds the cows, (or rather, evidence of their recent propinquity).

If Wally lies in the sun, he does not turn to a golden bronze. Last summer he fell asleep on the beach and got burned scarlet like a boiled lobster. He could not bear to put clothes on for two whole days.

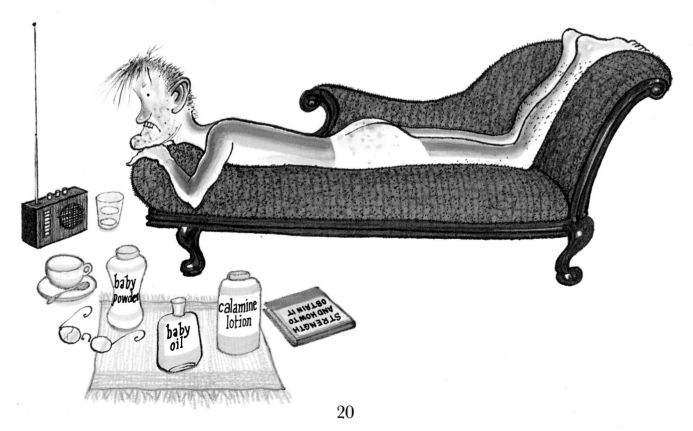

Wally tries to go brown to make himself more attractive, as he has never yet had a girl friend.

Once, long ago, he fell in love with the girl next door, Mavis Skinner, but when she

was sixteen she suddenly had a baby and married a Belgian butcher.

Across the street lives a very tall girl called Miss Eulalie Dobson. Wally wanted to ask her to

go to the pictures with him, but he discovered that she was going out with a very tall man

who had a red sports car with stereo speakers in it. This man also had his initials on

his number plates.

Wally has failed the driving test four times. He has never dared speak to Miss Dobson.

Recently, Wally read an advertisement for a "Bull-Basher Chest Expander." The picture
showed a muscley man bending a metal gadget while gorgeous girls smiled adoringly
at him. Wally sent for one. It cost £68 and he found he could not bend it at all.
He strained his groin and had to go to the Doctor for some Groin Strain Ointment.

Wally then thought he would make himself feel more glamorous by buying some jazzy nylon underpants.

Two weeks later, the Doctor told him it was these garments which had caused the Dhobi Itch in his crutch. Nylon does not allow the sweat to flow freely, you see.

He has now gone back to wearing baggy white cotton drawers like his Dad. His Mum buys them for him.

Wally's Mum also knits all his jumpers and woollies. He has seventeen items of home-made knitwear; from big manly sweaters in chunky-knit to fancy little waistcoats with pretty buttons. Unfortunately, his Mum always makes them far too small for him.

"My! How you've grown, Wallace!" she always says. "Aren't your hands getting big!"

"Mum," says Wally. "I'm twenty-nine."

Last summer, Wally's Uncle Bill and Auntie Katie took him out for a ride in their little motor boat. Wally was asked to sit at the front to balance it. He clung to the guard rails and was quite frightened by the throb of the engine and the splash of the waves.

On the way back, a big wave came suddenly from the side and soaked Wally's trousers. Everyone in the cockpit thought this very funny.

When they went ashore in the dinghy Wally thought he would be brave and dashing, so he sprang boldly out, clutching the rope. Unfortunately, his wellingtons stuck fast in the mud and the boat hit him in the bottom.

Later that year, when having tea at their Auntie Lizzie's, Wally's baby nephew refused to play

with his new Space Hopper.

All the relations were trying to encourage the little lad, so Wally thought he would show

them how it was done. He seized the horns of the hopper and bounced about,

feeling rather foolish – then suddenly he fell off. He felt a sharp stab of pain in his back

and his denture shot out onto the grass.

The little boy was delighted. He clapped his hands, stamped his feet and cried

"More! More!"

Then he stamped on Wally's denture.

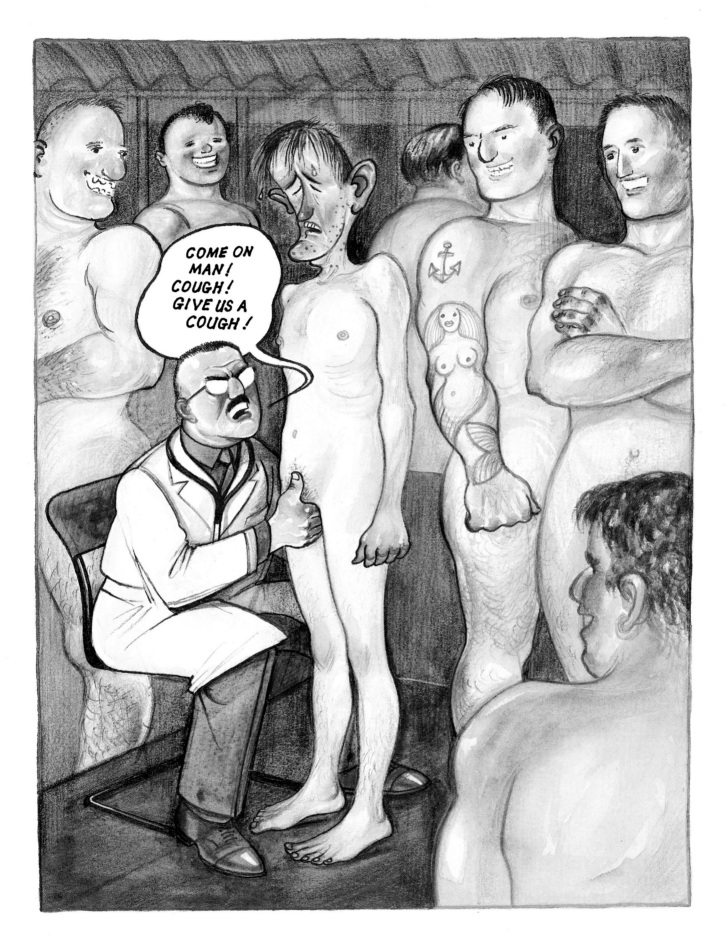

Some years ago Wally decided to join the Army.

He thought it might make a man of him, but of course, he failed the Medical.

By the way, no hairs have ever grown on Wally's chest.

Their absence has always rather worried him.

Also, when he was a boy, his voice broke very late.

In the choir, he sang with the little boys until he was eighteen.

In order to make himself look more manly, Wally once decided to grow a beard. Unluckily, the beard came out rather patchy and the moustache was a curious olive-green colour. Wally decided to dye it all blonde. He thought it might make him look like a Viking, but instead the dye brought him out in a violent rash of spots.

Although Wally could not grow a beard, hair grows vigorously where he does not want it.

Three hairs grow persistently from the tip of his nose and these have to be shaved.

Hair also sprouts from inside his nose and he has to trim it with scissors. This can be very

awkward, but Wally has perfected a technique which uses a mirror to reflect the sun's rays

up his nostrils. On occasion, his Mum has come into the room and caught him with the

scissors half way up his nose. For some reason Wally finds this rather embarrassing.

Despite all these failures, Wally remains quite un-selfconscious. He often picks his nose in public and he is also constantly wiggling his little finger in his ear, then removing it to gaze searchingly at the nail, (presumably to examine its contents). He does this in the middle of conversations and even during meals. In the same way, he never blows his nose without minutely scrutinising the handkerchief afterwards.

He is quite unaware of the harmful effect these habits have upon his social life.

Wally is rather clumsy and he is always knocking things over.

His hands are red and too big for his thin white arms.

His feet are too big for his thin white legs and even in winter, they are sweaty and smelly.

Although he is not fat, Wally does sweat more than most people. In summer, there are always big wet patches round his armpits.

He also has a minor speech defect: he cannot say "th."

He always says "f" or "v" instead.

At home Wally talks to himself out loud. In public, he limits himself to a subdued muttering.

Wally has a runny nose. It is often dripping and he is always sniffing.

He also bites his nails and picks at the side of his thumb until it sometimes becomes quite sore and unsightly.

When worried, he chews the inside of his lower lip. These rapid jaw movements produce a peculiar grimacing expression which has alarmed a number of people.

It happens quite often as Wally is almost always worried.

Although still quite young, Wally has a sprinkling of grey hairs and is already going slightly bald.

As has already been indicated, he has four false teeth, too.

He suffers from Indigestion.

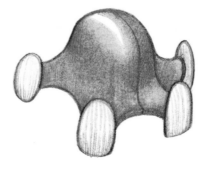

He also has Bad Breath

and Foul Bowels.

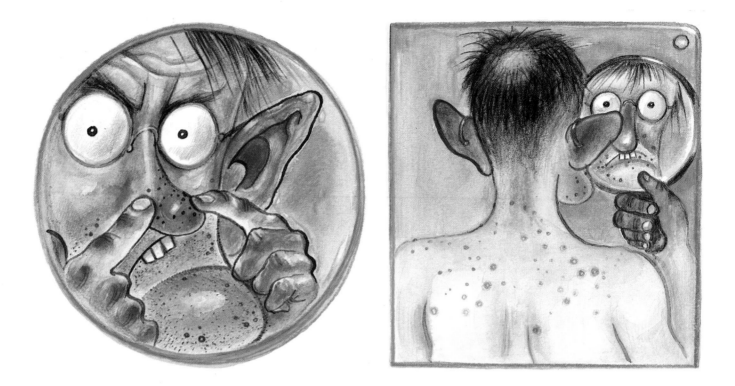

Blackheads cluster on his nose and Whiteheads spread across his shoulders and neck.

To his horror, Wally recently discovered tiny Varicose Veins on his ankles! Could this be a sign of ageing? *Already?*

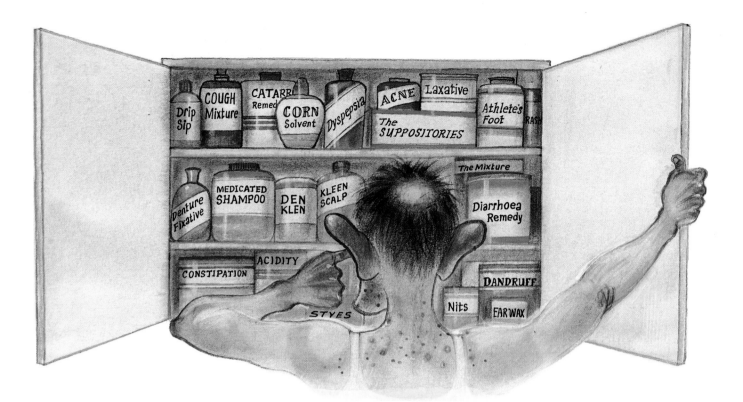

Wally has many other Minor Ailments; too numerous and too unpleasant to mention here, such as: Dandruff, occasional Boils on the back of his neck, Corns on his feet, Wax in his ears, Styes on his eyes, Warts on his hands and knees, the Dhobi Itch in the crutch, already mentioned, (see page 25) and Piles* – all very common complaints.

He is always very worried about his health and he visits the Doctor about once a fortnight.

*Haemorrhoids

Once Wally even started worrying about his Testicles, because he noticed they were not level.
He found that the right-hand one was ⅜ inch (or 9 millimetres) lower than his
left-hand one. He used his Dad's spirit level to measure accurately and was so nervous that
he pricked himself quite painfully in the thigh with a pair of school dividers.

His Doctor assured him, rather wearily, that all testicles were unevenly disposed and it was
not something he should lie awake at night fretting over.

The other day, Wally borrowed a book from the Public Library called "Symptoms."
The first night after reading it he did not sleep at all. The second night he slept only fitfully,
after returning from the doctor's with his list.

He is now worried that he may become a Hypochondriac. But Wally's Mum only says,
"My Wallace has always known how to take good care of himself."

As if to bear this out Wally has recently become a Health Food Addict. For breakfast every morning he eats a huge bowl of Bran. This is supposed to regulate his Bowels which are usually too much one way or the other.

He then eats his Mum's greasy eggs and even greasier bacon. Wally's Mum does not object to his health food as long as he eats it *in addition* to her meals.

44

Wally's Mum is very proud of him because he works in an "Office."

She bought him an expensive brief case made of real leather and he takes it to work every

day, even though it contains nothing except his sandwiches and a banana.

    Wally's Mum does not call it "going to work;" she calls it "going to business."

Women tend to think Wally is not really "a man." Men tend to agree with them.

However, he does not give offence to anyone (except by his Bodily Odours) and he has

never been in trouble with the police. He does not smoke and he drinks only Dubonnet

diluted with Lemonade. When at home, he likes to have a cherry in it, on a little stick.

Wally is not really disliked by anyone, but then he is not really *liked* by anyone either;

except for his Mum and Dad –

47

and Wally's Mum and Dad think he is wonderful.

48